The BFF TEST
Supersecret Questions to Share

by **ELIZABETH BENNETT**

Interior illustrations by
ANGELA MARTINI

SCHOLASTIC INC.

TO Lisa, Martha, Noreen, and Paula, who are always there to answer my questions.

ISBN 978-0-545-53060-6

12 11 10 9 8 7 6 5 4 3 2   12 13 14 15 16 17/0

Printed in the U.S.A.   40
This edition first printing, October 2012
Book design by Jennifer Rinaldi Windau

Contents

Calling All Gal Pals

This book is extra special because it's not just for you. It's for you *and* your friends! It's filled with quizzes and questions that will help you learn more about yourself and your gal pals. Some of the questions will make you think. Some of them will make you laugh. So grab a pencil and a gaggle of girlfriends and get going. No matter what your answers are, you can be sure of two things: You're going to learn a lot about friendship, and you're going to have a lot of fun!

Look through the next few pages and pick a spot that speaks to you!

NAME _____

PHONE NUMBER _____

CELL NUMBER _____

E-MAIL ADDRESS _____

❀ My favorite flower is a ❀

_____.

*Roses are red.
Violets are blue.
Friends are like flowers.
I picked one for you.*

NAME _____

PHONE NUMBER _____

CELL NUMBER _____

E-MAIL ADDRESS _____.

The TV show I never miss is _____

I wish I could meet this TV star: _____

_____.

NAME _____

PHONE NUMBER _____

CELL NUMBER _____

E-MAIL ADDRESS _____

My stage name will be _____.

I promise to send you tickets to see me

walk down the red carpet!

NAME _____

PHONE NUMBER _____

CELL NUMBER _____

E-MAIL ADDRESS _____

MY PET'S NAME IS _____.

THE PET I WISH I HAD

IS A _____.

We were "mint" to be together.

NAME _____

PHONE NUMBER _____

CELL NUMBER _____

E-MAIL ADDRESS _____

I would even share my

_____ with you.

(FAVORITE CANDY)

6

NAME _____

PHONE NUMBER _____

CELL NUMBER _____

E-MAIL ADDRESS _____

Favorite accompaniments:

( ) plain cone ( ) sugar cone ( ) sprinkles

( ) hot fudge ( ) cherry ( ) whipped cream

Favorite ice cream flavors: _____

My life is like an open book!

NAME _____

PHONE NUMBER _____

CELL NUMBER _____

E-MAIL ADDRESS _____

My dream job is:

( ) librarian ( ) author ( ) editor

I'll meet you after the game!

_____

NAME _____

PHONE NUMBER _____

CELL NUMBER _____

E-MAIL ADDRESS _____

My proudest sports moment is

_____ .

7

★ ★ ★ VOTE FOR ME! ★ ★ ★

NAME _____

PHONE NUMBER _____

CELL NUMBER _____

E-MAIL ADDRESS _____

When I am
President of the United States,
★ ★ I will: _____.★ ★

NAME _____

PHONE NUMBER _____

CELL NUMBER _____

E-MAIL ADDRESS _____

Things I love to do with my friends:

( ) SHOP   ( ) WATCH MOVIES

( ) TEXT   ( ) STUDY

( ) EAT PIZZA   ( ) HANG OUT

⊡ Fashion is my life! ⊡

NAME _____

PHONE NUMBER _____

CELL NUMBER _____

E-MAIL ADDRESS _____

My favorite outfit is

_____.

FRiENDSHiP METER QUiZ

Are you a crowd-pleaser, or a quiet observer?

How many friends is the right number for you?

Here's a quick quiz to figure it all out!

1. What do you think is the perfect number of friends?

 A. Three or four is the magic number.

 B. The more the merrier.

 C. Two's company, but three is a crowd.

2. On a Saturday afternoon, you like to:

 A. Get your homework done. Maybe you will have
 time to see a friend on Sunday.

 B. Go to a movie with a group of
 friends. And then maybe they can
 all sleep over!

 C. Invite a couple of friends over to
 listen to music. It's always fun
 when you get together.

Good for time indicated
DOWN UNDER
3:30 PM SAT
ADULT $10.00
Theaters
09/24/12
09/24/12

3. When you walk into the school cafeteria, you:

 A. Look for a quiet place to sit. Lunch is a time to
 take a break from a hard school day.

 B. Sit with the girls you have been sitting with since
 the second grade. You know you can count on them.

 C. Search out the table with the largest and noisiest
 crowd. That's where the action is!

4. Your birthday is next month. To celebrate, you plan to:

    A. Invite twelve of your closest friends for a slumber party with pizza, popcorn, and a bunch of movies!

    B. Ask your best friend to join your family for dinner at your favorite Japanese restaurant.

    C. Invite three friends to a day at the beach. It will be fun to hang out together!

5. In Spanish class you are asked to learn about a Spanish food and present it to your class. Your teacher says you can work alone or in a group. You:

    A. Can't decide which of your friends you want to work with. Maybe your teacher will let you work with a really big group. That way you won't hurt anyone's feelings.

    B. Team up with one friend to research your project. She can come over after school this week so you can work on it together.

    C. Work on your presentation by yourself. You don't mind working alone and it will be easier to get it done that way.

6. Today is the day to sign up for school sport teams. You plan to:

    A. Skip the sign-ups. You are already busy with ballet and piano lessons.

    B. Sign up for the school swim team. All those years in the pool will really pay off!

    C. Sign up for the soccer team. All your friends are going to try out as well!

Now, tally your score:

1. Give yourself 2 points if you answered A, 3 points if you answered B, or 1 point if you answered C.

	A)	B)	C)
2.	1	3	2
3.	1	2	3
4.	3	1	2
5.	3	2	1
6.	1	2	3

Total score: ☐   What does your score say about you?

6-9: Solo Act. You treasure the friendship of your closest friends, but you also value time alone. You are a good listener and take your responsibilities seriously. You tend to be drawn toward girls who are more on the quiet, shy side. Knowing that you are always there for one another is what keeps your friendships going.

10-14: True Blue. Once you make a friend, that friendship is for keeps. You have had some friends since kindergarten. You and your pals love one another's company more than anything else. Just hanging around together beats an organized outing. Your friends are always fun to be around and know how to make the most dreary day special!

15-18: Crowd-Pleaser. You and your friends love to be at the center of an activity. You are outgoing and always looking for a new adventure. You have a large circle of friends, but you still know how to make the "new girl" feel welcome. Nothing is more important to you than your friends!

PAL POLL

How much do you know about your best friend?
How much does she know about you? Take this quiz
about your friend, then pass the book to her so she can
answer the same questions about you.

1. The thing my friend **likes the most** about herself is

    _____ .

2. My friend's **most prized possession** is_____

    _____ .

3. She would be **least likely** to do the following
    in front of a crowd:

    A. Sing a solo.   B. Give a speech.   C. Dance.

4. Her mother's first name is _____ .

5. My friend's **birthday** is _____ .

6. When it comes to snacks, her all-time **favorite** is:

    A. French fries.   B. Pizza.

    C. Ice cream.   D. Other:_____ .

7. She was born in _____ .

    (city or town)

8. She would say it is **most important** to be:

    A. Rich.   B. Fashionable.   C. Smart.

Now it is your friend's turn to answer with you in mind:

1. The thing my friend **likes the most** about herself is

_____.

2. My friend's **most prized possession** is_____

_____.

3. She would be **least likely** to do the following

   in front of a crowd:

   A. Sing a solo.   B. Give a speech.   C. Dance.

4. Her mother's first name is _____.

5. My friend's **birthday** is _____.

6. When it comes to snacks, her all-time **favorite** is:

   A. French fries.   B. Pizza.

   C. Ice cream.   D. Other: _____.

7. She was born in _____.
   (city or town)

8. She would say it is **most important** to be:

   A. Rich.   B. Fashionable.   C. Smart.

SCORING:

Take a moment to score each other's quizzes. Give one point for each correct answer.

Add your answer totals together to get your friendship score!

10-16: Wow! You sure do know a lot about each other! It is obvious that you are both good listeners, and that's what friendship is all about! Keep up the good work!

5-9: You know each other pretty well, but you are always discovering new things about each other. Keep up the communication. The more you learn about each other, the better friends you will become!

0-4: Maybe this is a new friendship, or else you just haven't spent a lot of time together. Here's a chance to let your friendship take off. Ask lots of questions and be a good listener, and you may be on your way to making a new BFF (Best Friend Forever)!

PARTY PERFECTION!

You'll need a few of your friends to complete this hilarious story about the perfect party. Take turns calling out words to fill in the blanks. When you have written in all the words, read the story out loud. Try not to laugh too hard!

I'm so _____! Today is the day of my
     (adjective)

_____ party! I have invited _____ of my
  (noun)   (number)

_____ friends. I asked each one to bring a
  (adjective)

_____ and a _____. First, we are going to play
 (noun)   (animal)

_____. When we are done, we will make _____,
  (sport)   (food)

which we will eat with the pizza my _____ will be
                                  (relative)

delivering. After dinner we will listen to _____ and
                                  (noun)

_____. Mom promised to pop a _____ bowl of
  (verb)   (adjective)

popcorn and I rented a _____ called "My _____
                (noun)   (relative)

is a _____" for us to watch. Before bed we will tell
   (noun)

_____ stories and try to _____ one another.
  (adjective)   (verb)

It will be the most perfect party ever!

15

Go With the Flow!

How would your friends describe you?

Follow the flow to find out!

YES → Are you good at keeping secrets? ← NO

Do you daydream at school?

YES

NO →

Do you spend more than a half hour a day texting friends?

NO

YES →

Do your friends come to you NO with their problems?

YES

Does your teacher often ask you to walk your sick classmates to the nurse?

YES

NO →

Have you ever gotten in trouble for talking in school?

YES

NO →

Do you love animals more than movies?

YES

NO

SENSITIVE SWEETHEART.
Friends would describe you as sweet, caring, and kind.

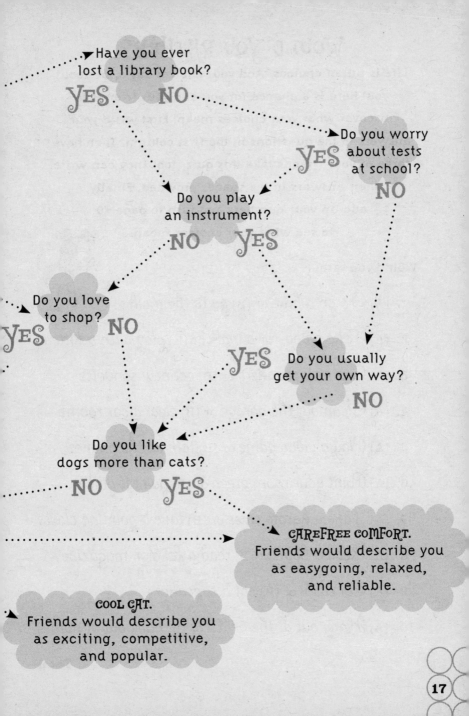

Have you ever lost a library book?

YES   NO

Do you worry about tests at school?

YES   NO

Do you play an instrument?

NO   YES

Do you love to shop?

YES   NO

Do you usually get your own way?

YES   NO

Do you like dogs more than cats?

NO   YES

CAREFREE COMFORT.
Friends would describe you as easygoing, relaxed, and reliable.

COOL CAT.
Friends would describe you as exciting, competitive, and popular.

WOULD YOU RATHER?

Life is full of choices. And your choices say a lot about you! Here is a chance for you and your friends to discover what your choices mean! First write *your* answers to the questions in the first column. Then have three of your friends take this quiz, too! They can write their answers in the spaces provided. Finally, add up your numbers and turn to page 20 to see what your choices mean.

Would you rather:

1. (A) Go on a hike or (B) go to the mall?

2. (A) Take a dog for a walk or (B) play with a kitten?

3. (A) Get new sneakers or (B) get new sandals?

4. (A) Clean out the garage or (B) clean your room?

5. (A) Play a video game or (B) talk on the phone?

6. (A) Paint your room green or (B) paint it pink?

7. (A) Take a karate class or (B) take a painting class?

8. (A) Read a book or (B) read a fashion magazine?

9. (A) Eat sushi or (B) eat a cupcake?

10. (A) Hang out at the beach or (B) hang out at home?

Total

You	Friend	Friend	Friend

You	Friend	Friend	Friend
—	—	—	—
—	—	—	—
—	—	—	—
—	—	—	—
—	—	—	—
—	—	—	—
—	—	—	—
—	—	—	—
—	—	—	—
—	—	—	—

ANSWERS:

Count up your total number of a's and B's.

If you got mostly a's: You are a bundle of energy and a busy bee. You have a large circle of friends who inspire and support you. You and your friends are always ready for a new adventure.

If you got mostly B's: You are easygoing and have a very relaxed personality. You tend to be on the quiet side, but you are open with those who are close to you. You treasure the friendship of girls who show they care. Nothing is more important to you and your friends than the time you spend together.

IF I WERE A . . .

If you were an animal, what kind of animal do you think you would be? What kind of flower? What kind of dessert? Your answers to these questions may reveal some interesting information about you. Circle your answers and then have some pals circle their answers using a different colored pencil or pen. Or, you can answer the quiz with some of your friends in mind. Remember to base your answers on what you think best describes you (or a friend), not what your favorite is. . . .

ANIMAL	FLOWER	INSTRUMENT
A. horse	A. daisy	A. trumpet
B. cat	B. lily	B. harp
C. tiger	C. rose	C. guitar
D. dolphin	D. lilac	D. violin
E. chimpanzee	E. sunflower	E. drums

DESSERT

A. apple pie

B. cream puff

C. double-fudge brownie

D. fresh fruit

E. chocolate-chip cookie

COLOR

A. green

B. pink

C. purple

D. red

E. yellow

SCHOOL SUBJECT

A. Math

B. Language Arts

C. Art

D. History

E. Recess

ICE CREAM FLAVOR

A. chocolate

B. strawberry

C. butter pecan

D. vanilla

E. mint chocolate chip

BOOK

A. thriller

B. poetry

C. fantasy

D. biography

E. humor

CITY

A. Sydney

B. Paris

C. Los Angeles

D. Rome

E. New York City

Answers revealed!

IF YOU ANSWERED MOSTLY A'S:

Sporty Girl. You have a very casual, relaxed style. You love to be outside or wherever else the action is. You are athletic, clever, and strong.

IF YOU ANSWERED MOSTLY B'S:

Girly Girl. You enjoy being a girl. Sweet and soft-spoken, you are caring and kind. You tend to be shy, but aren't afraid to be a little feminine.

IF YOU ANSWERED MOSTLY C'S:

Diva Queen. You love to be the center of attention. If it glitters or shines, it's for you. You tend to be competitive. Someday you hope to see your name in lights!

IF YOU ANSWERED MOSTLY D'S:

Brainiac. You are smart, sassy, and solid. You take your schoolwork seriously and have been known to read just for the fun of it. You also know how to relax and have fun.

IF YOU ANSWERED MOSTLY E'S:

Party Girl. You always make a splash and are a blast to hang out with. You are wise and witty, and can be counted on to lighten up any situation!

IF YOU ANSWERED A LITTLE BIT OF EVERYTHING:

Renaissance Gal. There are many sides to your personality. You don't worry about fitting into a mold. With you, anything goes!

WHAT WOULD YOU DO?

What would you do for one thousand dollars?
Would you shave your head? Would you give up television?
Compare your choices with your friends' here.
You answer YES or NO in the first column. Then there is room
for three more friends to respond.

If someone offered you **ONE THOUSAND DOLLARS**, would you:

1. Eat a *worm*?

2. Agree to *stop talking* for a month?

3. *Shave* your head?

4. Swim with *sharks*?

5. Give up *candy*?

6. *Hula dance* in front of your whole school?

7. *Kiss* a slug?

8. Walk on a *tightrope*?

9. Wear a *clown* costume to school?

10. *Share a room* with your little brother for a year?

11. Drink *pickle* juice?

12. *Move* across the country?

13. Let a *snake* wrap itself around your neck?

14. Wear the same outfit to school for a *month*?

24

15. *Skydive* from an airplane?

YOU	FRIEND	FRIEND	FRIEND
—	—	—	—
—	—	—	—
—	—	—	—
—	—	—	—
—	—	—	—
—	—	—	—
—	—	—	—
—	—	—	—
—	—	—	—
—	—	—	—
—	—	—	—
—	—	—	—
—	—	—	—
—	—	—	—

Numerology

Did you know that your name says
a lot about who you are and who are
the best friends for you? In numerology,
the letters in your name are assigned numbers,
and the numbers are added up to make your
destiny number. Your destiny number is what
makes you and your friends unique.

Here's how it works:

Start by writing down your whole name — first, middle, and last. Every letter is assigned a number from 1 to 9. Add these numbers together to make your destiny number. This chart shows all of the letters in the alphabet and the numbers each letter corresponds to.

NUMBER ASSIGNMENTS

1	2	3	4	5	6	7	8	9
A	B	C	D	E	F	G	H	I
J	K	L	M	N	O	P	Q	R
S	T	U	V	W	X	Y	Z	

Let's say your name is Amelia Rose Schwartz.

Each letter in your first name gets a number.

A	M	E	L	I	A
1	4	5	3	9	1

Add these numbers together.

$$1 + 4 + 5 + 3 + 9 + 1 = 23$$

If you end up with a number greater than 9, you add the digits together again.

$$2 + 3 = 5$$

Do the same for your middle name and last name.

R	O	S	E
9	6	1	5

$$9 + 6 + 1 + 5 = 21$$

$$2 + 1 = 3$$

S	C	H	W	A	R	T	Z
1	3	8	5	1	9	2	8

$$1 + 3 + 8 + 5 + 1 + 9 + 2 + 8 = 37$$

$$3 + 7 = 10$$

$$1 + 0 = 1$$

Now add the numbers from each part of your name together. Remember, if the answer is greater than 9, you will add the digits together again.

$$5 + 3 + 1 = 9$$

The destiny number for Amelia Rose Schwartz is **9**.

NOW IT IS YOUR TURN!

. . . .

NUMBER ASSIGNMENTS

1	2	3	4	5	6	7	8	9
A	B	C	D	E	F	G	H	I
J	K	L	M	N	O	P	Q	R
S	T	U	V	W	X	Y	Z	

. . . .

Write your name here: _____

Write a number for each letter in your first name here:

_____

Add the numbers together: _____

Write a number for each letter in your middle name here:

_____

Add the numbers together: _____

Write a number for each letter in your last name here:

_____

Add the numbers together: _____

First name total: _____

Middle name total: _____

Last name total: _____

Overall total (keep adding the numbers together if the total is greater than 9): _____

Your destiny number: _____

Okay, so now you know your destiny number. What does it say about you?

Destiny Numbers Revealed!

1 *is ambitious, independent, and self-sufficient.*

2 *is supportive, fair, and thoughtful.*

3 *is enthusiastic, optimistic, and fun loving.*

4 *is practical, traditional, and serious.*

5 *is adventurous, outgoing, and brave.*

6 *is responsible, careful, and quiet.*

7 *is independent, creative, and a bit of a loner.*

8 *is goal oriented, focused, and confident.*

9 *is enthusiastic, compassionate, and outgoing.*

Now you know what your number says about you. But here comes the fun part. What does your number say about friendships and who are the best friends for you?
Gather together a bunch of your friends and show them how to find their destiny numbers. Then check out the charts on the following pages. Pair up your results to see your friendships' true colors!

YOU	HER	
1	1	Almost twins. You are so much alike, you sometimes fight. Be careful.
1	2	A nice match. Don't take your friendship for granted.
1	3	Never a dull moment when you two are together. Have fun.
1	4	You two sometimes disagree. Respect each other's opinions.
1	5	Your friendship is always changing. You know how to keep things fun.
1	6	You can always count on each other. Make time for other friends, too.
1	7	You keep each other on your toes. What are you going to try next?
1	8	You share the same dreams. Work together to make them come true.
1	9	You two are very different. But that's what makes your friendship fun.
2	1	A nice match. Don't take your friendship for granted.
2	2	Two peas in a pod. You two are a perfect match.
2	3	You have different interests. Patience will keep your friendship strong.
2	4	A solid friendship. Don't forget to find the time for each other.
2	5	You have very different ways of going about things. Respect each other.

YOU	HER	
2	6	Very compatible. Give each other room to grow and develop.
2	7	You are both very busy. Make a special effort to get together.
2	8	You complement each other perfectly. Enjoy!
2	9	Friends one day, foes the next. Look for a happy medium.
3	1	Never a dull moment when you two are together. Have fun.
3	2	You have different interests. Patience will keep your friendship strong.
3	3	A wild ride. You never know what your next adventure will be.
3	4	A great friendship. Make sure you take time for other friends.
3	5	Fun, fun, fun. You know how to make each other happy.
3	6	You two enjoy quiet times together. Your friendship is important.
3	7	Even though you don't have a lot in common, you really get along.
3	8	You prove that opposites attract. You try hard to make it work.
3	9	Life is your stage! You both enjoy the spotlight.
4	1	You two sometimes disagree. Respect each other's opinions.
4	2	A solid friendship. Don't forget to find the time for each other.
4	3	A great friendship. Make sure you take time for other friends.
4	4	You have a strong friendship based on shared interests and opinions.
4	5	You have very different temperaments. Your friendship takes some work.
4	6	Like a cozy pair of pajamas, your friendship is as comfortable as it gets!
4	7	A serious friendship. Perhaps too serious. Try to lighten up!

YOU	HER	
4	8	School is important to both of you. That's great, but take time to relax.
4	9	An unlikely combination. Focus on things you have in common.
5	1	Your friendship is always changing. You know how to keep things fun.
5	2	You have very different ways of going about things. Respect each other.
5	3	Fun, fun, fun. You know how to make each other happy.
5	4	You have very different temperaments. Your friendship takes some work.
5	5	You each have different skills. Try to keep jealousy in check!
5	6	A great friendship. When you don't agree, compromise is the key.
5	7	Respect! You know how to give each other room to grow.
5	8	You inspire each other to be the best you can be!
5	9	An unusual combination. You both are always willing to try new things.
6	1	You can always count on each other. Make time for other friends, too.
6	2	Very compatible. Give each other room to grow and develop.
6	3	You two enjoy quiet times together. Your friendship is important.
6	4	Like a cozy pair of pajamas, your friendship is as comfortable as it gets!
6	5	A great friendship. When you don't agree, compromise is the key.
6	6	Your friendship is built on helping others. Take time for yourselves.
6	7	A difficult combination. Sometimes your personalities clash. Keep cool!
6	8	This friendship is for keeps. Make sure to take time for other friends.
6	9	Your friendship has some ups and downs. Work on keeping it light.

YOU	HER	
7	1	You keep each other on your toes. What are you going to try next?
7	2	You are both very busy. Make a special effort to get together.
7	3	Even though you don't have a lot in common, you really get along.
7	4	A serious friendship. Perhaps too serious. Try to lighten up!
7	5	Respect! You know how to give each other room to grow.
7	6	A difficult combination. Sometimes your personalities clash. Keep cool!
7	7	You two are so much alike! Try to search for individual differences.
7	8	Two very focused individuals. Slow down and find time to just have fun.
7	9	Friends since you first met. Treasure this friendship.
8	1	You share the same dreams. Work together to make them come true.
8	2	You complement each other perfectly. Enjoy!
8	3	You prove that opposites attract. You try hard to make it work.
8	4	School is important to both of you. That's great, but take time to relax.
8	5	You inspire each other to be the best you can be!
8	6	This friendship is for keeps. Make sure to take time for other friends.
8	7	Two very focused individuals. Slow down and find time to just have fun.
8	8	The Dynamic Duo. Just make sure to take time for yourself.
8	9	This friendship takes a little work. Keep at it. It will be worth it.
9	1	You two are very different. But that's what makes your friendship fun.
9	2	Friends one day, foes the next. Look for a happy medium.

YOU	HER	
9	3	Life is your stage! You both enjoy the spotlight.
9	4	An unlikely combination. Focus on things you have in common.
9	5	An unusual combination. You both are always willing to try new things.
9	6	Your friendship has some ups and downs. Work on keeping it light.
9	7	Friends since you first met. Treasure this friendship.
9	8	This friendship takes a little work. Keep at it. It will be worth it.
9	9	You have a very deep bond. You will always be there for each other.

Don't worry too much if it seems like you and your best friend aren't destined to live happily ever after. Friendships are always changing and growing. The important thing is that you care, and enjoy each other's company as much as you can!

Swap Section

The Swap Section is a really fab way to see how much you and your friends know about one another. It's a great activity to do at a birthday party, a sleepover, or even during recess! Do you think you will be able to recognize who your friends are by the way they answer these questions? Here's what you do:

✱ Gather together up to seven of your friends.

✱ Pass this book to one of your friends and ask her to secretly choose one of these symbols: ♥ ★ ❀ 🍃 ⌒ ❋ ♦ ☺

✱ Now ask her to read each question in the Swap Section and write her answer next to her symbol.

✱ When she is done, she will pass it to the next friend. Have everyone use the same pen so no clues are given.

✱ When all of your friends have answered the questions, it is your turn to answer them (use whatever symbol is leftover).

✱ Now the fun part starts! Pass the book back around and give everyone a chance to see if she can figure out which symbol belongs to which friend. There is a page at the end of the section for each of you to write your guesses.

Did you get any of the names right? What a great way to get to know each other!

1. WOULD YOU RATHER BE A FAMOUS SINGER, ACTOR, OR ATHLETE?

2. IF THEY MADE A MOVIE OF YOUR LIFE, WHAT ACTRESS WOULD PLAY YOU?

3. HOW LONG DOES IT TAKE YOU TO GET
READY FOR SCHOOL IN THE MORNING?

4. WHO IS YOUR ALL-TIME FAVORITE CARTOON CHARACTER?

5. WHAT IS YOUR FAVORITE THING TO DO
WITH YOUR FRIENDS?

 _____

 _____

 _____

 _____

 _____

 _____

 _____

 _____

6. IF YOU COULD ONLY EAT ONE FOOD FOR THE REST OF YOUR LIFE, WHAT WOULD IT BE?

HECE OF CLOTHING DO YOU
YOU COULD WEAR EVERY DAY?

♥ _____

★ _____

✿ _____

🍂 _____

🌈 _____

✳ _____

◆ _____

☺ _____

42

8. IF YOU WERE A PERFORMER
IN A CIRCUS, WHAT KIND OF ACT
WOULD YOU DO?

9. WHAT BOOK HAVE YOU READ OVER AND OVER AGAIN?

10. IF YOU COULD TRAVEL
ANYWHERE IN THE WORLD,
WHERE WOULD YOU GO?

 _____

 _____

 _____

 _____

 _____

 _____

 _____

 _____

45

11. IF SOMEONE WROTE YOUR LIFE STORY, WHAT WOULD THE TITLE BE?

12. WHAT GIVES YOU THE CREEPS?

13. WHAT ARE YOU MOST LIKELY TO FIND AT THE BOTTOM OF YOUR BACKPACK?

 _____

 _____

 _____

 _____

 _____

 _____

 _____

 _____

14. WHERE DO YOU USUALLY DO YOUR HOMEWORK?

♥ _____

★ _____

✿ _____

🍃 _____

🌈 _____

✳ _____

◆ _____

☺ _____

15. WHAT IS YOUR USUAL BEDTIME ON A SCHOOL NIGHT?

♥ _____

★ _____

✿ _____

🌿 _____

🌈 _____

✳ _____

◆ _____

 _____

50

FIGURE IT OUT

Now it's time to look over everyone's answers. Write your guesses in the spaces below. There is room for all of your friends to write their predictions. Then comes the big reveal! Who got the most correct answers?

Who do you think was the:

LOCKER NOTES

The rest of this book is filled with special notes
for you to fill out, tear out, and shout out
to a friend! Slip them into a friend's locker,
backpack, or math book. Just don't get caught
passing one to a friend in class!

Dear _____,

Do you want to come over after school today?

Meet me at _____ _____.

Can't wait to see you!

Love,

_____

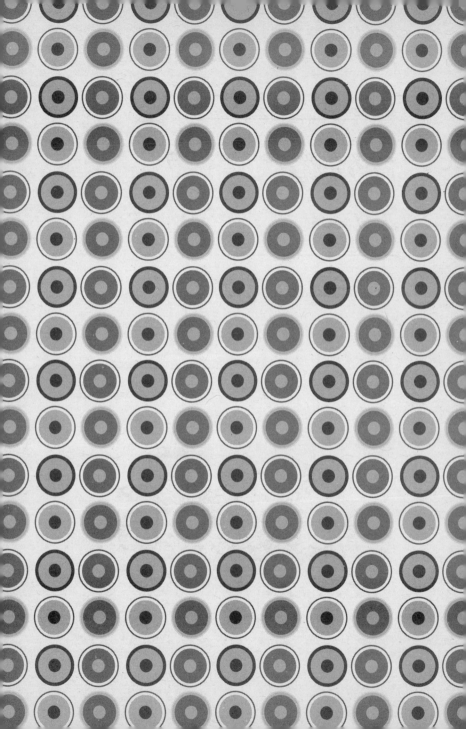

Dear _____,

I have a big problem! Do you think you can help me?

Call me today after school so we can talk.

Your friend,

_____

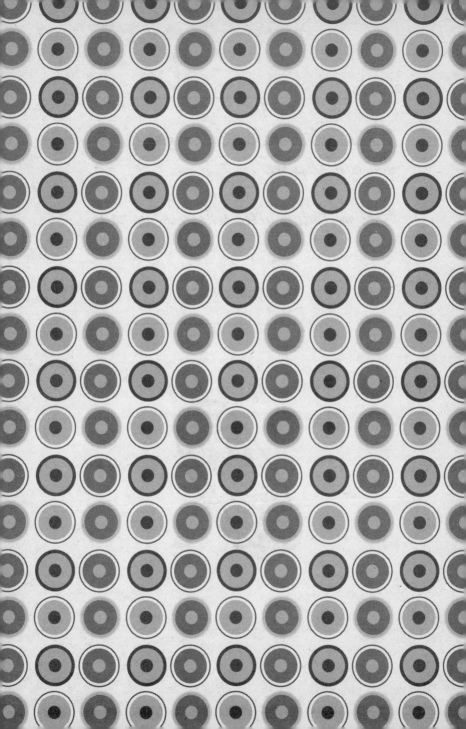

Dear _____,

Can you come for a sleepover this weekend?

That would be too cool!

Later!

_____

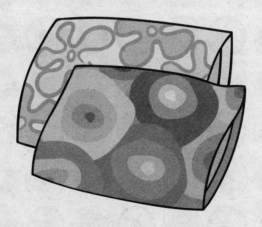

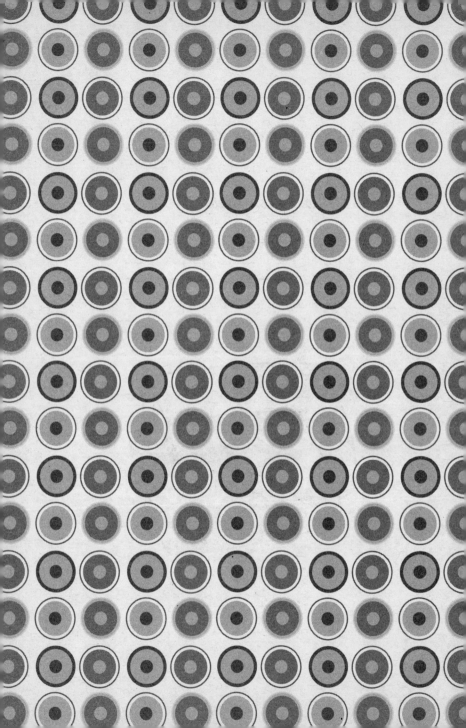

Dear _____,

I am so sorry for what happened. Will you ever forgive me?

I will call you today after school.

Your friend forever,

_____

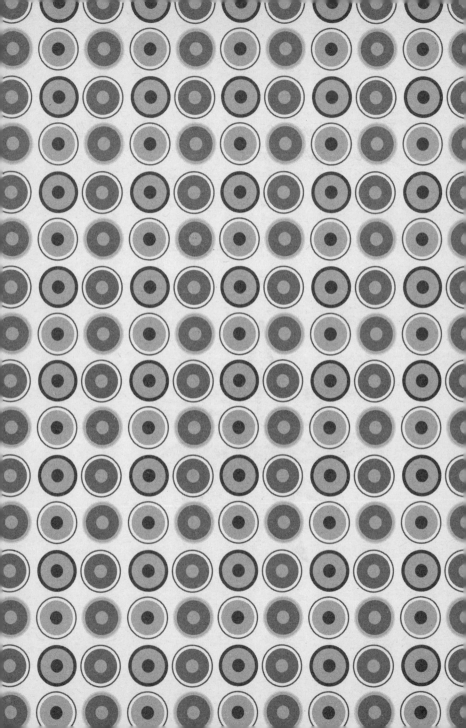

Dear _____,

I'm going to the movies this weekend. I really want to see

_____

_____

Do you want to come? I'll buy the popcorn!

       See ya,

       _____

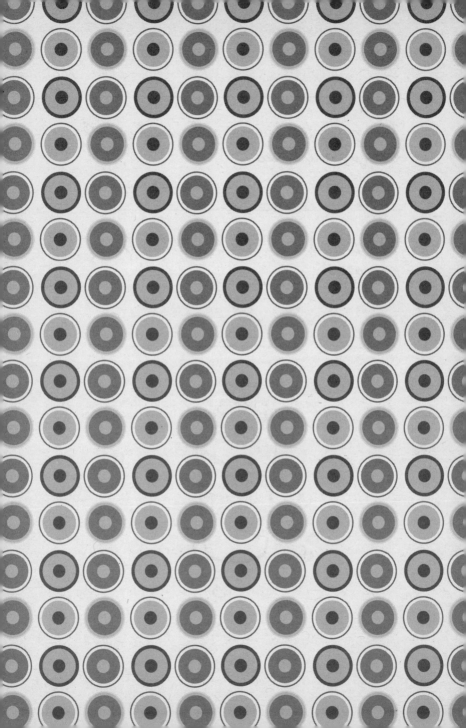

Dear _____,

My mom promised to take me to the mall on Saturday.

Do you want to come?

We'll have a blast!

Your fashionable friend,

_____

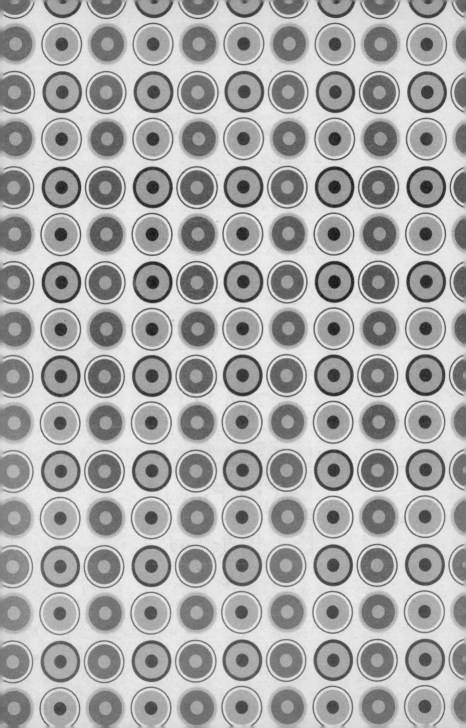